JUST BRASS

directed by

Philip Jones and Elgar Howarth

TUBA SOLOS
VOLUME ONE

arranged and edited by

JOHN FLETCHER

CONTENTS

This volume is available in versions for Tuba in C, E♭ Bass and BB♭ Bass

CHESTER MUSIC

TUBA SOLOS

arranged and edited by John Fletcher

1.

THE POLICEMAN'S SONG

from *The Pirates of Penzance*

Arthur Sullivan

* Play only if the tuba needs to rest here.

2.
SANCTUS

from *Grande Messe des Morts*

Hector Berlioz

3.
WHEN BRITAIN REALLY RULED THE WAVES

from *Iolanthe*

Arthur Sullivan

4.
DER LINDENBAUM
(The Linden Tree)

Franz Schubert

5.
HEY-HO, COME TO THE FAIR

(But Don't Be Silly)

Easthope Martin

6.
OH, IS THERE NOT ONE MAIDEN BREAST?

from *The Pirates of Penzance*

Arthur Sullivan

7.
VARIATIONS ON A TEMPERANCE THEME

(Father's a drunkard and Mother is dead)

Mrs. E.A. Parkhurst

18

VARIATION I

Waltz time [♩ = 120]

VARIATION II

VARIATION III

JUNIOR JUST BRASS

directed by Philip Jones & Elgar Howarth

An exciting new series from Chester Music which provides interesting and flexible ensemble music for less experienced players. Most of the works in the series will be in 4 or 5 versatile parts with optional percussion where suitable.

This blend of arrangements and original pieces so far includes:

1 JJB SUITE Elgar Howarth
2 trt hn trbn

2 JJB THREE LITTLE SUITES Peter Lawrance
2 trt hn 2 trbn

3 JJB FOUR CAROLS arr Rory Boyle
2 trt hn bass trbn/tuba perc

4 JJB FOUR CAROLS arr Rory Boyle
2 trt hn bass trbn/tuba perc

5 JJB SEVEN MOODS AND DANCES Stephan de Haan
2 trt hn trbn perc

6 JJB POPS FOR FOUR Chris Hazell
2 trt hn trbn perc

7 JJB THREE NORWEGIAN TUNES Grieg
arr Peter Reeve 2 trt hn trbn bass trbn/tuba perc

8 JJB THREE MINIATURES Ian MacDonald
2 trt hn bass trbn/tuba

9 JJB MISCELLANY ONE David S. Morgan
2 trt hn trbn

10 JJB THREE LATIN AMERICAN DANCES
Bruce Fraser 2 trt hn trbn perc

11 JJB BASED ON THE BLUES Dave Perrottet
2 trt hn trbn bass trbn/tuba

Alternative treble and bass clef parts are provided for trombones, as are parts for Eb horn, Eb bass and BBb bass wherever practicable.

More details from:

CHESTER MUSIC